Printed and bound by Blissetts of London
www.blissetts.com

CELEBRATING
100
YEARS 1920|2020

First Printing, 2020
ISBN 978-1-913719-07-4

Goldcrest Books International Ltd
publish@goldcrestbooks.com
www.goldcrestbooks.com

Enjoy our book!
M + KW

Introduction

This is the first book in a collection of the Time2Play stories and educational activities for children. All books are designed to support the development of young children. Parents, guardians and educators will find great pleasure in guiding children through the book. The fun begins with joint reading, followed by an educational discussion before the creative activities.

What is Time2Play?

We help children to learn, laugh and play, as they gain new skills and build positive friendships. We provide educational activities and games that promote positive life values and life skills essential for child development. Teamwork is necessary, and everyone will be encouraged to celebrate their achievements through joint play. This can be parents interacting and supporting their child or child-to-child play in the group. It is the teacher or play practitioner's responsibility to ensure everyone is included within the class.

Time2Play stories aim to:

Promote reading from an early age with our collection of books

Encourage self-expression and creative writing for future success

Encourage conversations to build social confidence

Encourage positive and healthy experiences with each other

Time2Play

MARC'S FIRST VISIT

This book is inspired by Marc, who is adventurous, loving and funny!

Marc woke up one bright Saturday morning, wanting to have fun and play with some friends.

He climbed out of bed and stretched.
Just then, he remembered the class his
friend went to. Marc went to find his mum.

"Mummy, can we go to my friend's class today?" Marc was hoping his mum would say yes.

Mum smiled, "Of course we can! Once you have put away your toys from last night and have breakfast." Marc felt excited and ran off to tidy up.

"Finished! Can we go now?"
He asked with a cheeky grin.

Marc thought he was smart by completing his chores quickly. Mum replied, "It's important we eat first, so not yet Marc."

Marc felt so excited, he could not eat all of his breakfast. He ran off to get ready. Mum met him at the front door. "Do you want me to help you put your shoes on?" she asked, but he had already started.

Off they went, all dressed and ready to go. On the way, Marc kept asking if they were nearly there. Each time Mum replied, "Not yet Marc!"

MARC 1

Time2Play

When they arrived, Marc looked through the car window and saw lots of colours on the grass. He wondered what they were for.

9

Marc and his mum got out of the car and walked towards the class. Marc was curious and pointed, "Mummy the grass has spots!"

Welcome Everyone!
Time2Play

Mum was puzzled and said, "Really?"

Marc said, "Yes! Yes! Look, the grass has spots... GREEN, BLUE, YELLOW." He found it funny and started giggling.

Mum waved as she got closer to the teacher and said hello.

Marc was still curious and ran ahead.
He got on his knees to find a spot.
A **BLUE** spot, then a **RED** spot.
He picked up a YELLOW spot and
guess what he did?

Hmm, I wonder what this smells like?

He sniffed it. Yes, he sniffed the spot! "Eww, it's stinky."

He ran to the teacher and asked, "What are we going to do with the spots?"

The teacher bent down to him and smiled, "Ah, that's a surprise! First, we have to be a little patient and wait for the children to arrive."

Marc felt so excited, he couldn't wait for the others to arrive. He was bursting with energy. If he were a balloon, he would pop!

He was impatient. He started to run around and chase the birds to pass the time. Mum shouted, "Be careful! You could fall!"

Soon, more parents and children started to arrive.
Marc and his mum both smiled.

The teacher blew her whistle
as the class song played in the
background. "It's time to begin!"

She welcomed Marc and his mum to the group and reminded everyone to use kind hands, kind feet and kind words.

"Let's warm up before we play the games. Well... I can see Marc already started when he ran SUPER fast earlier." Marc laughed, feeling pleased the teacher noticed him.

"I want all the children to dance to the music, then run to a red spot when the music stops," the teacher said. "Is everyone ready?"

"Yes!" the children shouted.

As the music played, the children danced. When the music stopped, they ran as fast as they could to find a red spot.

The parents were happy and the children were happy too. Marc was very, very, happy. He was having lots of fun.

The teacher said, "We are going to play a game called Popcorn. I would like you to all hold onto the side of the parachute. Let's shake it, and see how many balls stay on."

She threw the balls onto the parachute. Marc was so excited he was jumping up and down. As he did the balls were falling off.

Marc's mum and some of the children quickly picked them up and threw them on again. It was hard work!

Marc's Mum felt very tired. She said, "Phew! I think I need to sit down. My legs are wobbly!"

Wobble, wobble, wobble

Marc laughed.

Mum went off to sit down with wobbly legs.

Wobble, wobble, wobble.

Out of breath and with rosy cheeks, they gathered around the teacher. She asked, "Who had fun?"

The children shouted out, "Me! Me!"

She smiled, "I am proud of everyone because you showed great teamwork. We all deserve a high five!"

Mum thanked Marc for choosing the class today. They both had fun. She reminded him about the importance of being patient. She grinned and said, "All things come to those who wait." Marc giggled.

I wonder what he will get up to next time?

Exercise Your Mind and Activities

Now you have read the story, please complete the activities. Children can choose how they share their answers.

Activity Tools

You will need a writing pencil, coloured pencils and something to write on.

Getting Support

Choose an adult within the group (decide how many people will be in your group).

Activity Instructions

Adults will support children´s learning style and level of understanding in each activity. Children will develop at their own pace and allow for equal turn taking in a group. Remember to be patient!

There are three activities to complete. Each activity is divided into two age groups: children under 5 years old and children over 5 years old. Guided learning can be flexible with some encouragement for independent working.

Activity One: Let´s Talk

Talk about the life values and life skills highlighted. An example from the story is shown to help you.

Activity Two: Answer the Questions

Answer the questions from the story.

Activity Three: Creative Writing

Re-write or draw your own story of Marc's first visit to a Time2Play class.

Activity One: Let´s Talk

Children under 5 years old

Adults will help children to talk about the life values and life skills highlighted.

Communication
E.g. Marc and his mum **spoke** about the class. He also spoke with the teacher.
Q: Can you tell me who do you speak with at home or at school?

Happiness
E.g. Marc felt **happy** and **excited** in the class.
Q: Can you tell me what things make you happy?

Senses (We have five senses in our bodies: taste, touch, hearing, smell and sight).
E.g. Marc **touched** the spots and he **smelled** the spots.
Q: Think about your favourite fruit. What does it look like? Does it have a smell?
What does it feel like? What does it taste like? Does it have a sound when it is eaten?
(e.g. crunchy).

Teamwork
E.g. The children held the parachute **together.**
Q: Have you ever played games with others in a group?

Patience
E.g. Marc had to **wait** for the class to start.
Q: Can you tell me a time when you have been patient?

Praise
E.g. The teacher **praised** everyone for working as a team.
Give your grown-up a high five for working as a team on this worksheet. Well done!

Activity One: Let´s Talk

Children over 5 years old

Adults will help children talk about the life values and life skills highlighted.

Curiosity
E.g. Marc sniffed the spot because he **wondered** what it smelled like.
Q: Can you tell me what things have a bad smell?

Thinking Skills
E.g. Marc **thought** about what he wanted to do.
Q: Can you tell me a time you had made a decision?

Enjoying and Achieving
E.g. The children were **playing** and **having fun.**
Q: What fun games do you like to play?

Independence
E.g. Marc got dressed **by himself.**
Q: What task have you completed without any help?

Learning
E.g. The children **listened** and **learnt** how to play different games.
Q: How important is it to listen to others?

Praise
E.g. The teacher **praised** everyone for working as a team.
Give your grown-up a high five for working as a team on this book. Well done!

Activity Two: Answer the Questions

Children under 5 years old

Adults will help the children to answer the questions below.

Q: What part of the story did you like?

Q: What breakfast do you like to have in the morning?

Q: Can you tell me why it is important to have kind hands?

Q: Do you think Marc was happy or sad in the story?

Q: Marc's mum had wobbly legs. What do you think she should do?

Q: What things can we do when we are happy?

Q: What fun places have you been to?

Activity Two: Answer the Questions

Children over 5 years old

Adults will help the children to answer the questions below.

Q: What part of the story was your favourite?

Q: There are life values described in the story. Can you name two of them?

Q: Why is it important to work as a team?

Q: What games do you play outside?

Q: Can you tell me about a time when you made a decision?

Q: Who do you share your happy feelings with?

Q: What fun places have you been to?

Activity Three: Creative Writing

Children under 5 years old

Adults will support children in sharing their ideas and being creative.

Can you tell your grown-up a new story about Marc at Time2Play?

Or

Can you draw a picture from the Time2Play story? (Use your colours)

Children over 5 years old

Can you re-write the story of Marc at Time2Play?

Or

Can you draw a picture from the Time2Play story? (Use your colours)

Well done for completing this book!

Time2Celebrate

The authors **@KidsTime2Play** will publish children's stories or pictures on their Instagram and Facebook pages. If you would like your child to take part and you agree to the privacy notice, please email your child's story or picture to:

kidstime2play@hotmail.com

Acknowledgements

We would like to give a special thank you to all the friends and family who have supported us along this new journey. Another big thank you to Facet Therapy for the inspiration and the concept of Time2Play. You can find out more about the fantastic work they do with children, young people and families at: www. facettherapy.co.uk.

L☺☺K out!
For more adventures with Marc in the new Time2Play books.

www.kidstime2play.co.uk

Time2Play: Marc's First Visit

About the Authors

Marcia Rowe has many roles in her life. She is a wife, mother to Marc in the Time2Play stories; as well as a Registered Accredited Therapist with the British Association for Counselling and Psychotherapy (BACP) since 2006. Marcia has over 25 years of counselling experience and has been running successful businesses since 2005. She first set up Time2Talk Counselling in 2005 before her launch of Facet Therapy Ltd in 2014. The services offer a variety of therapeutic ways to connect with children, young people and families using approved theories and models. Marcia also holds an Affiliate Membership with some of the top international Private Medical Insurance (PMI) companies to provide counselling to their employees.

Kelita Wood is an Associate Member of the Chartered Institute of Personnel & Development (CIPD) and has an MA in Human Resources (2010). She is a Director of Feed Me Good CIC which runs health and well-being projects in the UK. She is the founder of Kids Employability Skills, which equips children with the right tools in life so they can achieve their future aspirations. Kelita has been involved in running children's activities for Virgin Active and Time2Play before becoming the Business Manager for Facet Therapy in November 2019. As a mum of two, Kelita's mission is to empower her own children and other young people with life skills and life values to become great citizens and employable adults.